Mr Keeping had a snake.
Mr Keeping went out with Bruce the snake.

1

Mr Keeping went to get some fish and chips.
Bruce the snake went too.

Mr Keeping went to see Fred.
Bruce the snake went too.

Mr Keeping went to the shop.
Bruce the snake went too.

Jamila was putting apples into a pile.
Mr Keeping bought a bag of apples.

5

'They are good apples,' said Jamila.
'Are they for Bruce?'
'No,' said Mr Keeping, 'they are not for Bruce.
I will have all the apples.'
He gave the money to Jamila.

Bruce looked at the apples.
He was not happy.
He wanted some apples.

7

Bruce went on the table by the window.
Mr Keeping left the apples in his bag.
Bruce could not get the apples.

Bruce looked out of the window.
He could see the shop,
and he wanted some apples.

Bruce went out of the window.
He went out into Wellington Square.

He went all the way to the shop to get
some apples.

Bruce saw the pile of apples.
The apples looked good.

12

Bruce went for the apples,
but Jamila grabbed his tail.

Jamila went to see Mr Keeping with Bruce.
Mr Keeping was cross with Bruce.
'I have looked all over for you,' he said.

Mr Keeping talked to Jamila.
Bruce looked for the apples.

Mr Keeping was cross with Bruce,
but Bruce was happy.
The apples were good.